So you really want to learn

LATIN PREP

Workbook 1A

A.M. Wright

GALORE PARK

www.galorepark.co.uk

Published by Galore Park Publishing Ltd
19/21 Sayers Lane, Tenterden, Kent TN30 6BW

www.galorepark.co.uk

Text copyright © Anne Wright 2006
Illustrations copyright Galore Park 2006

The right of Anne Wright to be identified as the author of this Work has been asserted by her in accordance with sections 77 and 78 of the Copyright, Designs and Patents Act 1988.

Typography by Qué, Kent
Cover illustration by Ian Douglass

Printed and bound by CPI, Antony Rowe, Chippenham

ISBN-13:   978 1 902984 67 4

First published 2006, reprinted 2007, 2008

Details of other Galore Park publications are available at www.galorepark.co.uk

ISEB Revision Guides, publications and examination papers may also be obtained from Galore Park.

Introduction

These exercises will help you to practise and improve your grasp of Latin. Each exercise has been designed to reinforce what you have learned in the first five chapters of Latin Prep 1 (Galore Park, 2006) and focuses on **vocabulary**, **grammar** or **translation** work. Latin Prep Workbook 1B (ISBN-13: 9781905735143) reinforces the work covered in the second half of Latin Prep 1. Your teacher may want you to do some or all of the exercises, but each one is suitable for practice or revision. References to the new edition of Latin Prep 1 by Theo Zinn are shown by 'LP1', e.g. LP1 p.2 means page 2 of Latin Prep 1.

There is a strong focus on **grammar**, not just because over a quarter of the marks at Common Entrance are specifically based on grammar, but because you cannot produce accurate translations (at **any** level) unless you know what the words are doing and why!

How to use this book

If you are told to learn something, do so – thoroughly!

Vocabulary

✔ Learn the vocabulary for each chapter **before** you begin. When learning, try to think of English derivations (words which come from the Latin word). This will help you to remember what Latin words mean.

✔ Use vocabulary **flashcards** (Latin on one side, English on the other). This will help you to check your knowledge and focus on troublesome words. You can make your own or buy flashcards from ISEB – ask your teacher.

✔ Always remember to learn what **type** of word you are studying (noun, verb, conjunction, etc.).

✔ Always learn the **grammatical information** given (e.g., if you have to learn that **casa** means **house**, learn all the information given: **casa, -ae, f. = house**). This way you can work out all the other endings and will know what sort of words to use with it.

Grammar

✔ Always **learn** grammar thoroughly.

✔ Try to **practise** new grammar by explaining it to someone else (little brothers or sisters make good guinea pigs!). If you can explain grammar well, then you have learned it properly.

✔ **Recite** endings to yourself at regular intervals to keep them fresh (try reciting them in the shower or on the way to school).

Translation

✔ **Never guess!** Use the word endings to work out the meaning. The sooner you train yourself to concentrate on endings, the quicker you will be able to translate Latin well.

Marks

✔ The maximum number of marks available is shown at the side of the exercise. There is also a space for your score. Try to improve on your best score!

On page 46 you will find a sheet to record your scores for each chapter.

CHAPTER ONE
GRAMMAR WORK: nouns

LEARNING POINT 1a
✔ **Learn** the information about singular and plural nouns, **LP1 p.6**

Exercise 1.1
State whether the following nouns are singular or plural and then translate*:

1.	nautae		**(2)**	( )
2.	aqua		**(2)**	( )
3.	poeta		**(2)**	( )
4.	agricolae		**(2)**	( )
5.	feminae		**(2)**	( )
			TOTAL (10)	( )

Exercise 1.2
Change these nouns from the singular to the plural and translate the new form*:

1.	insula		**(2)**	( )
2.	patria		**(2)**	( )
3.	dea		**(2)**	( )
4.	filia		**(2)**	( )
5.	puella		**(2)**	( )
			TOTAL (10)	( )

Exercise 1.3
Change these nouns from the plural to the singular and translate the new form*:

1.	feminae		**(2)**	( )
2.	poetae		**(2)**	( )
3.	deae		**(2)**	( )
4.	insulae		**(2)**	( )
5.	agricolae		2)	( )
			TOTAL (10)	( )

*Note: All nouns are in the nominative case.

GRAMMAR WORK: the verb 'to be'

LEARNING POINT 1b
✔ **Learn** the verb 'to be', **LP1 p.7**

Exercise 1.4
Translate:

1.	es		(1)	( )
2.	sunt		(1)	( )
3.	estis		(1)	( )
4.	sumus		(1)	( )
5.	sum		(1)	( )
6.	she is		(1)	( )
7.	we are		(1)	( )
8.	you (pl.) are		(1)	( )
9.	you (s.) are		(1)	( )
10.	it is		(1)	( )

TOTAL (10) ( )

GRAMMAR WORK: verbs

LEARNING POINT 1c
✔ **Learn** amo by heart, **LP1 p.10**

Exercise 1.5
Translate these verbs:

1.	vocant		(1)	( )
2.	laboramus		(1)	( )
3.	habitas		(1)	( )
4.	pugnatis		(1)	( )
5.	festinat		(1)	( )
6.	you (pl.) build		(1)	( )
7.	we walk		(1)	( )
8.	she loves		(1)	( )

9.   you (s.) shout _____ **(1)** ( )

10.   they give _____ **(1)** ( )

TOTAL (10) ( )

Exercise 1.6

Look at the following list of verbs:

rogant	pugnamus	festino
laudas	cantat	aedificatis

Write down and translate [*N.B. there will be one left over*]:

1.   a 1st person plural verb

_____ **(2)** ( )

2.   a 3rd person singular verb

_____ **(2)** ( )

3.   a 2nd person singular verb

_____ **(2)** ( )

4.   a 2nd person plural verb

_____ **(2)** ( )

5.   a 1st person singular verb

_____ **(2)** ( )

TOTAL (10) ( )

Exercise 1.7

Translate these verbs and then give the 1st person singular form:
e.g. amas = you (s.) love; 1st singular = amo

1.   ambulatis

_____ **(2)** ( )

2.   clamamus

_____ **(2)** ( )

3.   laborant

_____ **(2)** ( )

4.   aedificas

_____ **(2)** ( )

5.   rogat

_____ **(2)** ( )

TOTAL (10) ( )

Exercise 1.8

Answer the following questions:

1. **neco** means 'I kill'. Give the Latin for 'we kill'.

   _____ **(1)** ( )

2. **amas** means 'you (s.) love'. Give the Latin for 'you (pl.) love'.

   _____ **(1)** ( )

3. **ambulat** means 'he walks'. Give the Latin for 'they walk'.

   _____ **(1)** ( )

4. **aedificamus** means 'we build'. Give the Latin for 'I build'.

   _____ **(1)** ( )

5. **datis** means 'you (pl.) give'. Give the Latin for 'you (s.) give'.

   _____ **(1)** ( )

   TOTAL **(5)** ( )

Exercise 1.9

Give the correct forms of the following verbs and translate:
(Remember that **sum** has a different set of endings to other verbs.)

1. 3rd person singular of amo _____ **(2)** ( )

2. 2nd person plural of sum _____ **(2)** ( )

3. 1st person plural of rogo _____ **(2)** ( )

4. 1st person singular of sum _____ **(2)** ( )

5. 3rd person plural of laudo _____ **(2)** ( )

   TOTAL **(10)** ( )

CONSOLIDATION

Exercise 1.10 Comprehension

Read the following passage carefully and answer the questions on it:

1	Titus	'salve. poeta es?'	
	Sextus	'nauta sum et pugno!'	
	Titus	'poeta sum et canto!'	
	Sextus	'quis est Marcus?'	
5	Titus	'Marcus est agricola. **non** laborat. et Aulus agricola est. Marcus et Aulus agricolae sunt.'	**non** = not

1. What does Titus say to Sextus? (line 1)

   _____ **(3)** ( )

2. What does Sextus reply? (line 2)

_____ **(3)** ( )

3. What is Titus' job? What action is he doing? (line 3)

_____ **(3)** ( )

4. Sextus asks about another man – who? (line 4)

_____ **(1)** ( )

5. What job does this man do? Is he lazy? Write down and translate the Latin
    phrase that tells you if he is. (line 5)

_____

_____ **(4)** ( )

6. What is Aulus? (line 5)

_____ **(1)** ( )

TOTAL (15) ( )

Exercise 1.11 Translation

Translate the following conversation:

1	Sextus	'Gaius et Tiberius poetae sunt?'
	Titus	'pugnant et clamant. nautae sunt.'
	Iulia et Laelia	'puellae sumus; ambulamus. et vos? puellae estis?'
	Cassia et Aurelia	'nos feminae sumus; cantamus.'
5	Aulus et Marcus	'Cassia et Aurelia cantant.'
	Titus	'feminae sunt et cantant; vos agricolae estis et laboratis.'

_____

_____

_____

_____

_____

_____

_____

_____

_____

_____

TOTAL (30) ( )

Exercise 1.12 Grammar

Read the following passage and answer the following questions on it:

Marcus	'ego clamo. agricola sum.'
Gaius et Tiberius	'nos pugnamus. nautae sumus. Cassia et Aurelia cantant.'
Sulpicia	'feminae sunt. Marcus clamat et vos pugnatis.'

1. Give examples of:

    a plural noun   a 2nd person plural verb

    _____ _____

    a 1st person singular verb   a 1st person plural verb   **(4)**   ( )

    _____ _____

2. Marcus says 'I am a farmer.' (agricola sum, line 1). What would you write instead of sum if you wanted to say 'You (s.) are a farmer'?

    _____ **(1)**   ( )

3. State the person of **clamat** (line 3). _____ **(1)**   ( )

4. Sulpicia says 'They are women' (feminae sunt, line 3). How would you say 'She is a woman'?

    _____ **(2)**   ( )

5. 'Cassia and Aurelia sing' (Cassia et Aurelia cantant, line 2). What verb would you write if only one woman was singing?

    _____ **(1)**   ( )

6. Marcus says 'ego clamo (line 1)'. What is the point of using **ego**?

    _____ **(1)**   ( )

7. Translate into Latin: Gaius is a poet. He sings.

    _____ **(5)**   ( )

8. Translate into Latin: The farmers work and you (s.) fight.

    _____ **(5)**   ( )

                                              TOTAL (20)   ( )

                       CONSOLIDATION TOTAL (65)   ( )

CHAPTER ONE	**MAXIMUM SCORE**	150/150	=	100%	
	MY SCORE	/150	=	%	

CHAPTER 2
GRAMMAR WORK: nouns

> **LEARNING POINT 2a**
> ✔ **Learn** the nominative, vocative and accusative endings (singular and plural) listed, **LP1 p.15**

Exercise 2.1

Fill in the table below:

	Singular	Plural		
Nominative	puella	puell _____	**(1)**	( )
Vocative	puell _____	puell _____	**(2)**	( )
Accusative	puell _____	puell _____	**(2)**	( )
The nominative is used for	_____		**(1)**	( )
The vocative is used for	_____		**(1)**	( )
The accusative is used for	_____		**(1)**	( )
The singular is used when	_____		**(1)**	( )
The plural is used when	_____		**(1)**	( )
		TOTAL	**(10)**	( )

Exercise 2.2

Fill in the table below. Give the correct **singular** ending, then change these nouns from the singular to the **plural**. Finally, **translate** the plural nouns:

	Case	Singular	Plural		
1.	acc.	hast _____	hast _____	**(3)**	( )
2.	voc.	ancill _____	ancill _____	**(3)**	( )
3.	nom.	poet _____	poet _____	**(3)**	( )
4.	acc.	de _____	de _____	**(3)**	( )
5.	nom.	puell _____	puell _____	**(3)**	( )
			TOTAL	**(15)**	( )

Exercise 2.3

Fill in the table below. Give the correct **plural** ending, then change these nouns from the plural to the **singular**. Finally, **translate** the singular nouns:

	Case	Plural	Singular		
1.	voc.	naut _____	naut _____		
				(3)	( )
2.	acc.	patri _____	patri _____		
				(3)	( )
3.	nom.	femin _____	femin _____		
				(3)	( )
4.	acc.	incol _____	incol _____		
				(3)	( )
5.	voc.	insul _____	insul _____		
				(3)	( )
			TOTAL	**(15)**	( )

TRANSLATION WORK

Exercise 2.4

Highlight the **subject** in green, the **verb** in green stripes and the **object** in red. Then translate. **REMEMBER:** put the verb at the end of the sentence and use a plural verb with a plural subject (e.g. poet**a** voca**t** *but* poet**ae** voca**nt**).

1. poetae nautam vocant.

_____ **(3)** ( )

2. dea filiam laudat.

_____ **(3)** ( )

3. agricola feminam vocat.

_____ **(3)** ( )

4. agricolae feminas vocant.

_____ **(3)** ( )

5. incola insulas amat.

_____ **(3)** ( )

6. puellam filia non necat.

_____ **(3)** ( )

7.   nauta feminam vocat.

_____ **(3)** ( )

8.   ancillas agricolae amant.

_____ **(3)** ( )

9.   agricolae ancillas amant.

_____ **(3)** ( )

10.   feminam deae vocant.

_____ **(3)** ( )

11.   The girl loves the inhabitant.

_____ **(4)** ( )

12.   The inhabitant loves the girl.

_____ **(4)** ( )

13.   The inhabitants love the girls.

_____ **(4)** ( )

14.   We love the sailor.

_____ **(3)** ( )

TOTAL **(45)** ( )

CONSOLIDATION

> **LEARNING POINT 2b**
> ✔ **Revise** verb endings and vocabulary 1 and 2, **LP1 pp.7, 10, 13, 26**
> ✔ **Re-read LP1 p.24**

Exercise 2.5 Comprehension

Read the following passage and then answer the questions on it:

> agricola ambulat sed non festinat. puellae festinant et agricolam vocant.
> 'agricola, festinamus; sed **cur** non festinas?' clamant.
> 'cantatis,' clamat agricola, 'sed ego aquam porto. ego laboro. non festino.'

cur = why?

1.   Is the farmer walking quickly in line 1? Pick out and translate the Latin phrase that shows this.

_____ **(3)** ( )

2. In line 1, who then appear and what do they do? _____

_____ **(3)** ( )

3. What do they ask? (line 2) _____

_____ **(3)** ( )

4. What is the farmer's answer? (line 3)

_____ **(3)** ( )

5. Do you think the farmer gives a good explanation for why he is not hurrying?

_____ **(3)** ( )

TOTAL (15) ( )

Exercise 2.6 Translation

Translate the following passage into good English:

> puellas incolae laudant sed puellas agricola non amat. 'vos cantatis sed ego
> laboro,' clamat. 'agricola sum et puellas non amo, filias non amo, feminas non
> amo, sed deam amo et laudo.'

_____

_____

_____

_____

_____

_____

_____

_____

(30) ( )

Exercise 2.7 Grammar

Read the following passage and then answer the questions on it:

> puellae clamant, 'agricola, puellas non amas. nos **igitur** agricolas non amamus.'
> puellae laborant et cantant. sed agricola non cantat – puellas et feminas non amat.

igitur = therefore

1. In which case is each of the following nouns and why?

(a) puellae (line 1) _____

_____ **(2)** ( )

(b) agricolas (line 1) _____ **(2)** ( )

2. In which person is each of the following verbs?

(a) amas (line 1) _____ **(1)** ( )

(b) cantant (line 2) _____ **(1)** ( )

3. Change **feminas** (line 2) into the accusative singular. _____ **(1)** ( )

4. In line 1, the girls say to the farmer, 'we do not like farmers' (agricolas non amamus). How would you change **amamus** if there were only one girl?

_____ **(1)** ( )

5. **clamant** (line 1). Translate this word and explain the connection between the Latin word clamant and the English word exclamation.

_____

_____

_____ **(3)** ( )

6. Translate into Latin: The women call the farmer.

_____

_____ **(4)** ( )

7. Translate into Latin: The farmer does not love girls.

_____

_____ **(5)** ( )

TOTAL **(20)** ( )

CONSOLIDATION TOTAL **(65)** ( )

CHAPTER TWO	MAXIMUM SCORE	150/150	=	100%
	MY SCORE	/150	=	%

CHAPTER 3

GRAMMAR WORK: genitive case, 1st declension

LEARNING POINT 3a
✔ **Re-read** the information on the genitive, **LP1 p.27** and **learn** the genitive endings

Exercise 3.1

Put the following nouns into the cases shown:

1.	puella	gen. pl.		**(1)**	( )
2.	incola	gen. pl.		**(1)**	( )
3.	aqua	gen. s.		**(1)**	( )
4.	poeta	gen. pl.		**(1)**	( )
5.	sagitta	gen. s.		**(1)**	( )
6.	agricola	acc. pl.		**(1)**	( )
7.	pecunia	gen. s.		**(1)**	( )
8.	nauta	nom. pl.		**(1)**	( )
9.	dea	voc. s		**(1)**	( )
10.	sagitta	acc. s.		**(1)**	( )
			TOTAL	**(10)**	( )

Exercise 3.2

Analyse the following sentences. Highlight the **nominative** in green, the **verb** in green stripes, the **accusative** in red, and the **genitive** in yellow. Then translate:

1. puella filiam nautae amat.

_____

_____ **(4)** ( )

2. puella pecuniam reginae portat.

_____

_____ **(4)** ( )

3. puellae pecuniam reginarum amant.

_____

_____ **(4)** ( )

4.   nauta filiam feminae portat.

_____

_____ **(4)** ( )

5.   nautae filias feminarum amant.

_____

_____ **(4)** ( )

6.   The girl carries the money of the poet.

_____

_____ **(5)** ( )

7.   The girls carry the spears of the poets.

_____

_____ **(5)** ( )

8.   The sailor does not love the money of the goddess.

_____

_____ **(5)** ( )

9.   The sailors love the money of the inhabitants.

_____

_____ **(5)** ( )

10.   The queen loves the inhabitants of the island.

_____

_____ **(5)** ( )

TOTAL (45) ( )

GRAMMAR WORK: dative case, 1st declension

> **LEARNING POINT 3b**
> ✔ **Re-read** the information on the dative, **LP1 p.29** and **learn** the dative endings, **LP1 p.27**

Exercise 3.3

Put the following nouns into the cases shown:

1.   puella   dat. s.   _____ **(1)** ( )

2.   aqua   dat. pl.   _____ **(1)** ( )

3.	sagitta	dat. s.	**(I)**	( )
4.	nauta	dat. pl.	**(I)**	( )
5.	insula	dat. pl.	**(I)**	( )
6.	dea	gen. pl.	**(I)**	( )
7.	ira	nom. pl.	**(I)**	( )
8.	agricola	acc. s.	**(I)**	( )
9.	sagitta	dat. pl.	**(I)**	( )
10.	incola	gen. s.	**(I)**	( )

TOTAL (10) ( )

Exercise 3.4

Highlight the **nominative** in green, the **verb** in green stripes, the **accusative** in red and the **dative** in blue. (No genitives are used.) Then translate.

Remember that **do** (I give) is often followed by a dative noun (e.g. I give the dog to the boy).

1.   puella nautae aquam dat.

(4) ( )

2.   puella nautis aquam dat.

(4) ( )

3.   puellae sumus et nautis aquam damus.

(6) ( )

4.   femina reginae non cantat.

(4) ( )

5.   cur reginae ancillis et nautis cantant?

(6) ( )

6.   incola feminae aquam dat.

(4) ( )

7. The sailor sings to the queen.

_____

_____ **(4)** ( )

8. We give money to the queens.

_____

_____ **(4)** ( )

9. The queen sings to the sailors.

_____

_____ **(4)** ( )

10. The women give the arrows to the sailors.

_____

_____ **(5)** ( )

TOTAL **(45)** ( )

GRAMMAR WORK: ablative case, 1st declension

LEARNING POINT 3c
✔ **Re-read** the information on the ablative, **LP1 p.29** and **learn** the ablative endings, **LP1 p.27**

Exercise 3.5

Put the following nouns into the cases shown:

1.	ira	abl. s.	_____	**(1)**	( )
2.	agricola	abl. pl.	_____	**(1)**	( )
3.	pecunia	abl. s.	_____	**(1)**	( )
4.	regina	abl. pl.	_____	**(1)**	( )
5.	ancilla	abl. pl.	_____	**(1)**	( )
6.	aqua	dat. pl.	_____	**(1)**	( )
7.	incola	abl. s.	_____	**(1)**	( )
8.	poeta	nom. pl.	_____	**(1)**	( )
9.	nauta	gen. s.	_____	**(1)**	( )
10.	patria	gen. pl.	_____	**(1)**	( )

TOTAL **(10)** ( )

Exercise 3.6

Highlight the **nominative** in green, the **verb** in green stripes, the **accusative** in red and the **ablative** in purple. Then translate.

1. nauta poetam hasta necat.

    _____

    _____ **(4)** ( )

2. nautae poetam hastis necant.

    _____

    _____ **(4)** ( )

3. ancillam dea sagitta necat.

    _____

    _____ **(4)** ( )

4. filiam aqua non necamus.

    _____

    _____ **(3)** ( )

5. ancillae feminas sagittis et hastis necant.

    _____

    _____ **(5)** ( )

6. The poet kills the girl with a spear.

    _____

    _____ **(5)** ( )

7. The poets kill the girls with spears.

    _____

    _____ **(5)** ( )

8. The girls kill the poets with a spear.

    _____

    _____ **(5)** ( )

9. The maid-servant kills the inhabitant with an arrow.

    _____

    _____ **(5)** ( )

10. We are poets. We do not fight with arrows.

_____

_____ **(5)** ( )

TOTAL (45) ( )

GRAMMAR WORK: genitive case, 2nd declension

LEARNING POINT 3d

✔ **Learn** the 2nd declension genitive endings, **LP1 pp.33, 36** and **38**

Exercise 3.7

Put the following nouns into the cases shown:

1.	servus	gen. pl.	_____	**(1)**	( )
2.	murus	gen. s.	_____	**(1)**	( )
3.	filius	gen. pl.	_____	**(1)**	( )
4.	liber	gen. pl.	_____	**(1)**	( )
5.	deus	gen. s.	_____	**(1)**	( )
6.	filius	acc s.	_____	**(1)**	( )
7.	servus	acc. pl.	_____	**(1)**	( )
8.	vir	gen. s.	_____	**(1)**	( )
9.	equus	gen. s.	_____	**(1)**	( )
10.	puer	gen. pl.	_____	**(1)**	( )

TOTAL (10) ( )

Exercise 3.8

Analyse the following sentences. Highlight the **nominative** in green, the **verb** in green stripes, the **accusative** in red and the **genitive** in yellow. Then translate.

1. servus equum domini amat.

_____

_____ **(4)** ( )

2. servi equos dominorum amant.

_____

_____ **(4)** ( )

3. amici puerorum muros non aedificant.

_____

_____ **(4)** ( )

4.   puer filium domini vocat.

_____

_____ **(4)**   ( )

5.   servi dominorum filios vocant.

_____

_____ **(4)**   ( )

6.   The horses love the sons of the masters.

_____

_____ **(5)**   ( )

7.   The slave does not love the master of the horse.

_____

_____ **(5)**   ( )

8.   The horse loves the slave of the master.

_____

_____ **(5)**   ( )

9.   The son carries the food of the god.

_____

_____ **(5)**   ( )

10.   The sons carry the food of the gods.

_____

_____ **(5)**   ( )

TOTAL **(45)**   ( )

GRAMMAR WORK: dative case, 2nd declension

> **LEARNING POINT 3e**
> ✔ **Learn** the 2nd declension dative endings, **LP1 pp.33, 36 and 38**

Exercise 3.9
Put the following nouns into the cases shown:

1.   amicus   dat. s.   _____ **(1)**   ( )
2.   equus   dat. pl.   _____ **(1)**   ( )
3.   puer   dat. s.   _____ **(1)**   ( )
4.   servus   dat. pl.   _____ **(1)**   ( )
5.   dominus   dat. pl.   _____ **(1)**   ( )

6.	filius	dat. s.	_____	**(1)** ( )
7.	puer	nom. pl.	_____	**(1)** ( )
8.	servus	acc. s.	_____	**(1)** ( )
9.	deus	dat. s.	_____	**(1)** ( )
10.	equus	voc. pl.	_____	**(1)** ( )

TOTAL (10) ( )

Exercise 3.10

Highlight the **nominative** in green, the **verb** in green stripes, the **accusative** in red and the **dative** in blue. (No genitives are used.) Then translate.

1. filius amico equum dat.

_____ **(4)** ( )

2. magister pueris libros dat.

_____ **(4)** ( )

3. puer magistro libros dat.

_____ **(4)** ( )

4. pueri magistris cibum dant.

_____ **(4)** ( )

5. deus puero equum dat.

_____ **(4)** ( )

6. The boy carries the book for the man.

_____ **(5)** ( )

7. The boys do not sing to the teacher.

_____ **(5)** ( )

8. The man sings to the god.

_____ **(4)** ( )

20

CONSOLIDATION

9.   The men sing to the gods and the teacher.

_____

_____ **(6)**   ( )

10.   The teacher gives the food to the men.

_____

_____ **(5)**   ( )

                                      TOTAL (45)   ( )

GRAMMAR WORK: ablative case, 2nd declension

> **LEARNING POINT 3f**
> ✔ **Learn** the 2nd declension ablative endings, **LP1 pp.33, 36** and **38**

Exercise 3.11

Put the following nouns into the cases shown:

1.	deus	abl. s.	_____ **(1)**	( )
2.	amicus	abl. pl.	_____ **(1)**	( )
3.	ager	abl. s.	_____ **(1)**	( )
4.	cibus	abl. pl.	_____ **(1)**	( )
5.	murus	abl. pl.	_____ **(1)**	( )
6.	dominus	acc. pl.	_____ **(1)**	( )
7.	amicus	voc. s.	_____ **(1)**	( )
8.	deus	gen. pl.	_____ **(1)**	( )
9.	cibus	acc. s.	_____ **(1)**	( )
10.	equus	nom. pl.	_____ **(1)**	( )

                                      TOTAL (10)   ( )

CONSOLIDATION

Exercise 3.12 Comprehension

Read the following passage and answer the questions below:

> **Not everyone is working hard!**
>
> filius magistri non laborat; amicus filii etiam non laborat. pueri clamant et cantant. tandem magister filium vocat et rogat: 'fili, **cur** non laboras? muros agricolae aedificant. viri et feminae laborant. domini filia cibum portat et feminis dat. **cur** non laboras?'

cur = why

1. In line 1, which two people are not working? _____

    _____ **(4)** ( )

2. In lines 1-2, what do they do instead?

    _____ **(2)** ( )

3. Who intervenes in line 2 and after what length of time?

    _____ **(2)** ( )

4. Translate **fili, cur non laboras?** (line 2)

    _____ **(3)** ( )

5. What are the farmers doing? (lines 2-3)

    _____ **(2)** ( )

6. What **two** things does the master's daughter do to help? (lines 3-4)

    _____

    _____ **(2)** ( )

    TOTAL **(15)** ( )

Exercise 3.13 Translation

Translate the following passage:

> filius **non iam** cantat sed festinat. aquam portat et domino dat.
> **mox** servus intrat et clamat: 'domine, incolae insularum hic sunt.
> nautas sagittis necant.' ira domini **magna** est. dominus viros,
> feminas, pueros, puellas vocat.

non iam = no longer
mox = soon
magna = great

_____

_____

_____

_____

_____

_____

_____

_____

TOTAL (30)   (   )

Exercise 3.14 Grammar

Read the following passage and then answer the questions on it:

'incolae agros patriae **oppugnant**,' clamat, 'sed hastis pugnamus!' dominus et agricolae hastas portant et festinant. hastis pugnant. incolae tamen **multos** viros sagittis necant. tandem viri incolas hastis necant. dominus viros laudat. viris pecuniam et equos dat.	oppugno, -are = I attack **multos** = many

1. From the passage, give an example of:

    (a) a noun in the genitive _____ **(1)**   (   )

    (b) a 1st person plural verb _____ **(1)**   (   )

2. In which case are the following nouns and why?

    (a) sagittis (line 3) _____

    _____ **(2)**   (   )

    (b) viris (line 4) _____

    _____ **(2)**   (   )

3. State the Latin subject and object of **oppugnant** (line 1):

    Subject _____ Object _____ **(2)**   (   )

4. In line 4, we are told that 'the master praises the men' (dominus viros laudat). What changes would you make to **dominus** and **viros** if you wanted to say 'the masters praise the man'?

    _____

    _____ **(2)**   (   )

5. Give an English word derived from **equos** (line 4) and explain its meaning.

    _____

    _____ **(2)**   (   )

6. Translate into Latin: We give the money to the master.

    _____

    _____ **(4)**   (   )

7.   Translate into Latin: The daughters of the friends sing.

_____

_____ **(4)** ( )

TOTAL **(20)** ( )

CONSOLIDATION TOTAL **(65)** ( )

CHAPTER THREE	MAXIMUM SCORE	350/350	=	100%
	MY SCORE	/350	=	%

CHAPTER 4

GRAMMAR WORK: 2nd declension neuter nouns

LEARNING POINT 4a

✔ **Learn** the neuter as set out, **LP1 p.40**

Exercise 4.1

Change the nominative singular of the following neuter nouns to the case shown and then translate the new form. Note the use of three extra nouns which you will learn in Chapter 6:

auxilium, -i. n. = help **vinum, -i. n.** = wine **periculum, -i. n.** = danger

1.   periculum   gen. s. _____

_____ **(2)** ( )

2.   verbum   acc. pl. _____

_____ **(2)** ( )

3.   oppidum   abl. s. _____

_____ **(2)** ( )

4.   vinum   dat. pl. _____

_____ **(2)** ( )

5.   templum   voc. s. _____

_____ **(2)** ( )

TOTAL **(10)** ( )

GRAMMAR WORK: prepositions

LEARNING POINT 4b
✔ **Revise** the information on prepositions, **LP1 p.41**
✔ **Remember:** de can mean 'down from', 'concerning' or 'about' – choose the correct meaning to match the rest of the sentence

Exercise 4.2

Translate the following sentences. Note that not all sentences use prepositions:

1. in muro stamus!

    _____ **(3)** ( )

2. nautae in bellis pugnant.

    _____ **(4)** ( )

3. agricolae dominos insularum superant.

    _____ **(4)** ( )

4. fili, cur in oppido ambulas? cur non laboras?

    _____ **(7)** ( )

5. magister servos vocat et de ancillis rogat.

    _____ **(7)** ( )

6. We walk with friends.

    _____ **(4)** ( )

7. Sextus, why do you hurry out of the town?

    _____ **(6)** ( )

8. We fight in the war.

    _____ **(4)** ( )

9. Why do you (pl.) walk in the fields?

_____

_____ **(5)** ( )

10. The poets sing about the gods of the island.

_____

_____ **(6)** ( )

TOTAL (50) ( )

GRAMMAR WORK: adjectives

LEARNING POINT 4c
✔ **Read** the information on adjectives, **LP1 pp.43-45**
✔ **Remember** that you need to learn the gender of a noun in order to be able to produce the correct form of the adjective
e.g. agricola may look like a normal feminine 1st declension noun, but it is masculine, so you would have to use a masculine adjective (e.g. bonus) with it

Exercise 4.3

Translate these sentences:

1. nautae fessi ex aqua alta festinant.

_____

_____ **(6)** ( )

2. pueri mali in agro non laborant sed cum puellis laetis cantant.

_____

_____ **(10)** ( )

3. multi agricolae in templo oppidi sunt.

_____

_____ **(6)** ( )

4. ancillam bonam rogas, 'quis in insula magna pugnat?'

_____

_____ **(8)** ( )

5. incolas malos hasta magna necamus sed reginam bonam non necatis.

_____

_____ **(10)** ( )

6. The good daughter does not work.

_____

_____ **(4)** ( )

7. The tired girls praise the good goddess.

_____

_____ **(6)** ( )

8. You (pl.) kill the boy with many arrows.

_____

_____ **(5)** ( )

9. The happy friends do not fight.

_____

_____ **(5)** ( )

10. The tired sailors overcome the inhabitants.

_____

_____ **(5)** ( )

TOTAL **(65)** ( )

GRAMMAR WORK: sum + complement

LEARNING POINT 4d
✔ **Learn** the information on sum, **LPI p.46**

Exercise 4.4
Translate these sentences (not all of which use sum + complement):

1. ego bona sum, sed tu malus es.

_____

_____ **(7)** ( )

2. ubi sunt puellae laetae? puellae ex oppido ambulant.

_____

_____ **(8)** ( )

3. cur puer fessus est? in agro non laborat.

_____

_____ **(7)** ( )

4. templa alta et magna sunt.

_____

_____ **(4)** ( )

5. magistro multos libros damus.

_____

_____ **(4)** ( )

6. The good boy is a farmer.

_____

_____ **(5)** ( )

7. The good girl is tired.

_____

_____ **(5)** ( )

8. The good poets carry big books.

_____

_____ **(6)** ( )

9. Many women are in the big town.

_____

_____ **(6)** ( )

10. Where is the small temple of the goddess? It is here!

_____

_____ **(8)** ( )

TOTAL **(60)** ( )

GRAMMAR WORK: imperfect tense

Exercise 4.5
Translate the following verbs:

1. festinabamus _____ **(1)** ( )

2. intrabas _____ **(1)** ( )

3. aedificabant _____ **(1)** ( )

4.	pugnabam		**(1)**	( )
5.	laborabat		**(1)**	( )
6.	I was loving		**(1)**	( )
7.	they were asking		**(1)**	( )
8.	we were carrying		**(1)**	( )
9.	he was singing		**(1)**	( )
10.	you (s.) were building		**(1)**	( )
		TOTAL	**(10)**	( )

Exercise 4.6

Change the verb to the plural and translate the new form:

1. clamabam

    (2) ( )

2. aedificabas

    (2) ( )

3. laudabat

    (2) ( )

4. rogabas

    (2) ( )

5. necabam

    (2) ( )

    TOTAL **(10)** ( )

Exercise 4.7

Change the verb to the singular and translate the new form:

1. intrabamus

    (2) ( )

2. amabatis

    (2) ( )

3. vocabant

    (2) ( )

4. laborabamus

    (2) ( )

5. festinabant _____

    _____ **(2)** ( )

                                    TOTAL **(10)** ( )

Exercise 4.8

Translate these sentences. Remember that the imperfect can be translated as 'I was' or 'I used to'.

1. filiae deas laudabant sed ex oppido festinabamus.

    _____

    _____ **(7)** ( )

2. equis fessis aquam et cibum dabamus.

    _____

    _____ **(6)** ( )

3. amici magistri in agris cantabant. e templo festinabamus.

    _____

    _____ **(8)** ( )

4. de equis et de bellis magnis cantabant.

    _____

    _____ **(7)** ( )

5. feminae filium vocabant et de puellis rogabant.

    _____

    _____ **(7)** ( )

6. You (s.) were hurrying out of the town.

    _____

    _____ **(4)** ( )

7. We were calling the bad slaves.

    _____

    _____ **(4)** ( )

8. They used to live in the temple.

    _____

    _____ **(4)** ( )

9. The tired masters were shouting.

    _____

    _____ **(4)** ( )

10. You (pl.) were giving water to the horse.

_____

_____ **(4)** ( )

TOTAL **(55)** ( )

GRAMMAR WORK: imperfect tense of sum

LEARNING POINT 4f

✔ **Learn** the imperfect tense of sum, **LP I p.49**

Exercise 4.9

Translate into English or Latin as appropriate. Note that both present and imperfect tenses are used.

1.	eramus	_____	**(1)**	( )
2.	they were	_____	**(1)**	( )
3.	you (pl.) are	_____	**(1)**	( )
4.	you (pl.) were	_____	**(1)**	( )
5.	es	_____	**(1)**	( )
6.	we are	_____	**(1)**	( )
7.	eram	_____	**(1)**	( )
8.	sum	_____	**(1)**	( )
9.	eras	_____	**(1)**	( )
10.	erant	_____	**(1)**	( )

TOTAL **(10)** ( )

Exercise 4.10

Translate these sentences. Present and imperfect tenses may be used.
Note that quod means 'because'.

1. quod fessae eramus, in agris non laborabamus.

_____

_____ **(7)** ( )

2. quod magister bonus est, libros magnos portamus.

_____

_____ **(7)** ( )

3.   de regina poeta cantabat et regina laeta erat.

_____

_____ **(8)**   ( )

4.   filius feminae magnus erat.

_____

_____ **(4)**   ( )

5.   cibus servorum malus erat sed cibus ancillarum bonus est.

_____

_____

_____ **(9)**   ( )

6.   The girl used to be small.

_____

_____ **(4)**   ( )

7.   You (pl.) were happy.

_____

_____ **(3)**   ( )

8.   We were in the temple of the goddess.

_____

_____ **(5)**   ( )

9.   You (s.) used to give food to the boy.

_____

_____ **(4)**   ( )

10.   We give books to the boys.

_____

_____ **(4)**   ( )

                                      TOTAL (55)   ( )

CONSOLIDATION

Exercise 4.11 Comprehension

Read the following passage and answer the questions on it:

> **The war at Troy goes badly for the Greeks after a quarrel**
>
> <u>olim</u> in bello magno **Graeci** pugnabant. Achilles in bello pugnabat. Achilles puellam amabat. sed Agamemnon, **rex Graecorum**, etiam puellam amabat et **eam** multis verbis laudabat. tandem Agamemnon Achillem vocabat et 'puellam amo. ubi est?' rogabat.

olim = once
Graecus, -i, m. = Greek
rex = king
eam = her

1.   Who was fighting in line 1? _____ **(1)** ( )

2.   How did Achilles feel about the girl? (line 2) _____ **(1)** ( )

3.   Who was Agamemnon? How did he feel about the girl? _____

   _____ **(3)** ( )

4.   Write down and translate the phrase (line 3) that shows how Agamemnon showed his admiration for the girl.

   _____

   _____ **(5)** ( )

5.   What did he say about the girl in line 4?

   _____ **(3)** ( )

6.   What question did he ask of Achilles in line 4?

   _____ **(2)** ( )

                                                        TOTAL (15) ( )

Exercise 4.12 Translation

Translate the following passage:

1	Achilles laetus non erat. 'ancillam amo! ancilla **mea** est!' sed Agamemnon clamat, 'ego **rex** et dominus sum. ancillam **cupio**.' ira viri magna erat. domino tamen ancillam dat. **quod** Achilles non pugnabat, **Graeci nunc** in magno **periculo** erant. incolae de muris oppidi festinabant, **Graecos** superabant, multos in bello necabant.	**meus, a, um** = my, mine **rex** = king **cupio** = I want **quod** = because **Graecus, -i, m.** = Greek **nunc** = now **periculum, -i, n.** = danger
5		

                                                         TOTAL (30) ( )

Exercise 4.13 Grammar

Read and answer the questions on the following passage:

1	Patroclus 'cur, amice, non pugnas?' amicum rogat. '**quod** Agamemnon puellam **meam** **rapuit**, non pugno.' Patroclus **arma** amici **accipit** et ab amico festinat. tandem Hector ex oppido festinat et Patroclum necat. Achilles **miser** est et **Hectorem**
5	necat.

quod = because
meus, a, um = my
rapuit = snatched
arma = weapons
accipit = receives
miser = wretched, unhappy
Hectorem = Hector (acc.)

1. In what case is each of the following nouns and why?

   (a) amice (line 1) _____

   _____ **(2)** ( )

   (b) amici (line 3) _____

   _____ **(2)** ( )

   (c) amico (line 3) _____

   _____ **(2)** ( )

2. State the tense and person of **festinat** (line 3). _____

   _____ **(2)** ( )

3. Give the 1st person singular present tense of **est** (line 4). _____ **(1)** ( )

4. In line 1, 'Patroclus asks his friend' (Patroclus amicum rogat). What change would you make to **amicum** if you wanted to say 'Patroclus asks his **friends**'?

   _____

   _____ **(1)** ( )

5. In line 2, we are told that 'Agamemnon seized my girl' (Agamemnon puellam meam rapuit). What change would you need to make to **puellam** if you were to say 'Agamemnon seized my **girls**'?

   _____ **(1)** ( )

6. In lines 3-4, Hector hurries out of the town (Hector ex oppido festinat). What would you write if you wanted to say '**you (pl.)** hurry'?

   _____ **(1)** ( )

7. In line 4, we are told that 'Achilles is unhappy' (Achilles miser est). How would you change **est** if you wished to say 'Achilles and Agamemnon **are** unhappy'?

   _____ **(1)** ( )

8. Translate **Patroclum necat** (line 4). _____

   _____ **(2)** ( )

9. From the passage, give an example of:

   (a) a 2nd person s. verb _____ **(1)** ( )

   (b) an adverb _____ **(1)** ( )

   (c) a masc. acc. s. noun _____ **(1)** ( )

   (d) a conjunction _____ **(1)** ( )

10. Change **oppido** (line 4) into the nom. s. _____ **(1)** ( )

   TOTAL **(20)** ( )

   CONSOLIDATION TOTAL **(65)** ( )

CHAPTER FOUR	MAXIMUM SCORE	400/400	=	100%
	MY SCORE	/400	=	%

CHAPTER 5
GRAMMAR WORK: numbers

LEARNING POINT 5a
✔ **Read** and **learn** the information on numbers, **LP1 p.52**

Exercise 5.1

Translate these sentences:

1. una femina cum quattuor viris ambulabat.

   _____

   _____ **(6)** ( )

2. duae puellae in muris magni templi stant.

   _____

   _____ **(7)** ( )

3. puero septem equos dabamus.

   _____

   _____ **(4)** ( )

4. agricola quinque servos vocat et rogat, 'ubi est ancilla?'

_____

_____ **(8)** ( )

5. tria templa in oppido erant.

_____

_____ **(5)** ( )

6. We were praising seven farmers.

_____

_____ **(4)** ( )

7. The three boys are good.

_____

_____ **(5)** ( )

8. Six poets were killing four maid-servants.

_____

_____ **(6)** ( )

9. Two women dwell in the town.

_____

_____ **(6)** ( )

10. You (pl.) build nine temples.

_____

_____ **(4)** ( )

TOTAL **(55)** ( )

GRAMMAR WORK: prepositions + accusative

LEARNING POINT 5b
- ✔ **Revise** prepositions followed by an ablative, **LP1 p.41**
- ✔ **Learn** prepositions followed by an accusative, **LP1 p.53**
- ✔ Take especial care with in + acc (into/on to)
  in + abl (in/on)

Exercise 5.2

Translate the following sentences:

1. ad templum sex puellae festinant.

_____

_____ **(5)** ( )

2. servi in agros dominorum intrabant.

    _____

    _____ **(5)** ( )

3. amicus cibum per agros portabat.

    _____

    _____ **(5)** ( )

4. prope muros templi clamabamus et cantabamus.

    _____

    _____ **(5)** ( )

5. pecuniam reginae trans agros portabam.

    _____

    _____ **(5)** ( )

6. You (s.) were walking through the fields.

    _____

    _____ **(4)** ( )

7. The god of war dwells in the temple.

    _____

    _____ **(6)** ( )

8. The teacher walks into the temple.

    _____

    _____ **(5)** ( )

9. We were fighting near the temples of the inhabitants.

    _____

    _____ **(5)** ( )

10. You (pl.) used to sing about five wars.

    _____

    _____ **(5)** ( )

    TOTAL **(50)** ( )

GRAMMAR WORK: dative of the possessor

LEARNING POINT 5c

✔ **Learn** the information on the dative of the possessor, **LP1 p.54**

Exercise 5.3

Translate these sentences, not all of which use the dative of the possessor:

1. viris Romanis multi servi sunt.

   _____

   _____ **(5)** ( )

2. cur filia domino cibum dabat?

   _____

   _____ **(5)** ( )

3. deo equus magnus est.

   _____

   _____ **(4)** ( )

4. in insulis incolis pecunia multa erat.

   _____

   _____ **(6)** ( )

5. magistro novem libri magni sunt.

   _____

   _____ **(5)** ( )

   TOTAL (25) ( )

GRAMMAR WORK: perfect tense

LEARNING POINT 5d

✔ **Learn** the information on the perfect tense, **LP1 pp.55-56**

Exercise 5.4

Translate the following verbs:

1. ambulavistis _____ **(1)** ( )
2. clamavisti _____ **(1)** ( )
3. vocavimus _____ **(1)** ( )
4. necavit _____ **(1)** ( )
5. habitavi _____ **(1)** ( )
6. they loved _____ **(1)** ( )

7.	we gave	_____	**(1)**	( )
8.	he has worked	_____	**(1)**	( )
9.	you (s.) fought	_____	**(1)**	( )
10.	they have walked	_____	**(1)**	( )
		TOTAL	**(10)**	( )

Exercise 5.5

Change the verb to the plural and translate the new form:

1.   ambulavi   _____
     _____ **(2)** ( )

2.   amavisti   _____
     _____ **(2)** ( )

3.   portavit   _____
     _____ **(2)** ( )

4.   necavisti   _____
     _____ **(2)** ( )

5.   dedi   _____
     _____ **(2)** ( )

     TOTAL (10) ( )

Exercise 5.6

Change the verb to the singular and translate the new form:

1.   laudavimus   _____
     _____ **(2)** ( )

2.   vocavistis   _____
     _____ **(2)** ( )

3.   clamaverunt   _____
     _____ **(2)** ( )

4.   festinaverunt   _____
     _____ **(2)** ( )

5.   stetimus   _____
     _____ **(2)** ( )

     TOTAL (10) ( )

Exercise 5.7

Translate these sentences:

1.   octo nautas hastis necavimus.

_____

_____ **(4)** ( )

2.   ego deam laudavi sed vos deos laudavistis.

_____

_____ **(7)** ( )

3.   pueri libros novem per agros portaverunt.

_____

_____ **(6)** ( )

4.   magister reginae pecuniam multam dedit.

_____

_____ **(5)** ( )

5.   in templo stetisti et cum quinque ancillis cantavisti.

_____

_____ **(8)** ( )

6.   We fought in the war.

_____ In bello   pugravimus _____

_____ **(4)** ( )

7.   The Roman girls walked into the fields.

_____ puellae   romanae   in   agros   ambulaverunt _____

_____ **(6)** ( )

8.   You (s.) stood on the wall.

_____ in muro   stetisti _____

_____ **(4)** ( )

9.   The boys' master called the seven women.

_____ Magister puerorum   Septem feminas   vocavit _____

_____ **(6)** ( )

10. We built the walls of the big town.

_____ muros oppidi Magni   aedificavimus _____

_____ **(5)** ( )

TOTAL **(55)** ( )

GRAMMAR WORK: adjectives ending in -er

LEARNING LEARNING POINT 5e
✔ **Learn** the information about adjectives that end in –er, **LP1 p.57**

Exercise 5.8

Translate the following. Note that not all adjectives used end in –er.

1. feminae pulchrae dis sacris cibum dederunt.

    _____

    _____ **(6)** ( )

2. dominus servi malus est et servus miser erat.

    _____

    _____ **(7)** ( )

3. pueri magistro libros non dederunt. magister iratus erat.

    _____

    _____ **(8)** ( )

4. quattuor viri Romani cum filia pulchra cantabant.

    _____

    _____ **(7)** ( )

5. duae ancillae per agros hastas magnas portaverunt.

    _____

    _____ **(7)** ( )

6. You (s.) walk out of the beautiful temple.

    _____

    _____ **(5)** ( )

7. I carried many arrows.

    _____

    _____ **(4)** ( )

8. The god entered into the Roman temple.

    _____

    _____ **(6)** ( )

9.   Why did you (s.) kill the wretched slave?

_____

_____ **(5)**   ( )

10.   The son has eight horses. [N.B. *Use the dative of the possessor.*]

_____

_____ **(5)**   ( )

                                                    TOTAL (60)   ( )

GRAMMAR WORK: sum, perfect tense

LEARNING POINT 5f

✔ **Read** and **learn** the information about the perfect of sum, **LP1 p.59**

Exercise 5.9

Translate, using the correct forms of the verb **sum**:

1.   they have been/were _____ **(1)**   ( )

2.   you (s.) have been _____ **(1)**   ( )

3.   we have been/were _____ **(1)**   ( )

4.   you (pl.) have been _____ **(1)**   ( )

5.   he has been/was _____ **(1)**   ( )

6.   you (pl.) are _____ **(1)**   ( )

7.   it was (impf.) _____ **(1)**   ( )

8.   I was (impf.) _____ **(1)**   ( )

9.   they are _____ **(1)**   ( )

10.   I have been/was _____ **(1)**   ( )

                                                    TOTAL (10)   ( )

Exercise 5.10

Translate these sentences:

1.   fuit una femina pulchra.

_____ **(4)**   ( )

2.   amico novem sagittae fuerunt.

_____ **(4)**   ( )

3.   in bello sacro hastis multas nautas necavi.

_____ **(7)**   ( )

4.   puer in agro agricolae laboravit et fessus erat.

_____ **(7)**   ( )

5.   sagittis sacris pugnavistis.

_____ **(3)**   ( )

6.   We have been bad!

_____ **(3)**   ( )

7.   The walls of the towns were not beautiful [*N.B. use the perfect tense*].

_____ **(5)**   ( )

8.   The sons of the queen have been happy.

_____

_____ **(5)**   ( )

9.   I used to ask the queen about the beautiful islands.

_____

_____ **(6)**   ( )

10.   The slaves killed the Roman man with a spear.

_____

_____ **(6)**   ( )

TOTAL (50) ( )

CONSOLIDATION

Exercise 5.11 Comprehension

Read the following passage and then answer the questions on it:

> ### Who killed the poet?
>
> 1   regina Quintum vocavit et clamavit. 'Quinte, poeta **mortuus** est! quis poetam
>   magna hasta necavit?'
>   Quintus ad templum festinavit; feminas et viros vocavit. tres feminae pulchrae
>   et multi viri in templum intraverunt. Quintus de poeta rogavit, 'poeta
> 5   Romanus **mortuus** est. in templo eratis?'
>   una femina, Sulpicia **nomine**, clamavit, 'Marcus prope muros templi erat!'
>   Quintus Marcum rogavit. 'cur, Marce, prope templum eras?'
>   'prope muros laborabam sed templum non intravi! sed Sulpicia intravit!'

mortuus, a, um = dead

nomine = by name, called

---

1.   Who was killed and how? (lines 1-2) _____

_____ **(3)**   ( )

2.   Whom did Quintus call in line 3 and how many came? _____

_____ **(4)**   ( )

3.   What question did Quintus ask them? (lines 4-5) _____

_____ **(2)**   ( )

4.   Where did Sulpicia say that Marcus was? (line 6) _____

_____ **(2)**   ( )

5.   What did Marcus say that he was doing in line 8? _____

_____ **(3)**   ( )

6.   In line 8, who entered the temple, according to Marcus? _____

_____ **(I)**   ( )

TOTAL **(15)**   ( )

Exercise 5.12 Translation

Translate the following passage:

I Sulpicia clamavit, 'ego deam laudabam. deae cibum dabam! sed duo filii magistri etiam in templo erant!' Quintus ad pueros ambulavit. 'cur, pueri miseri, in templo eratis? cur poetam necavistis?' 5 'prope templum murus est. in muro stabamus. vir tamen ad murum ambulavit et, **quod** vir iratus erat, in templum festinavimus.' 'cur vir iratus erat?' 'templum sacrum est et in muro sacro stabamus.'	**quod** = because

_____

_____

_____

_____

_____

_____

_____

_____

_____

_____

TOTAL **(30)** ( )

Exercise 5.13 Grammar

Read the following passage and then answer the questions on it:

1	Quintus 'mali estis,' <u>**dixit**</u>. 'poetam tamen non necavistis. sed,' rogavit, 'quis erat vir iratus?' 'poeta erat! et servus cum poeta erat.' 'ubi est servus?' feminae clamaverunt. 5 'hic est,' agricola clamavit. 'serve, poetam hasta necavisti!' '<u>**minime**</u>!' Quintus clamavit, 'servus poetam non necavit! <u>**aliquis**</u> poetam bonum hasta magna necavit. sed de hasta non <u>**dixi**</u>. agricola de hasta <u>**dixit**</u>. poetam agricola malus necavit.'	**dixit** = he said/spoke **minime** = no **aliquis** = someone **dixi** = I said

1.   From the passage give an example of each of the following:

    (a) an adjective   **(1)** ( )

    (b) a 2nd person plural irregular verb   **(1)** ( )

    (c) a 3rd person singular perfect verb   **(1)** ( )

    (d) a verb in the imperfect tense   **(1)** ( )

2.   In which case is each of the following nouns and why?

    (a) serve (line 5)

                                                         (2) ( )

    (b) hasta (line 7)

                                                         (2) ( )

3.   State the subject and object of **necavit** (line 6).

    Subject   Object   **(2)** ( )

4.   Give an English word derived from **rogat** (line 1) and explain the connection

    between the English and the Latin words.

                                                               (3) ( )

5.   Translate into Latin: We carried the poet.

_____ **(3)** ( )

6.   Translate into Latin: The boys were praising the girls.

_____ **(4)** ( )

TOTAL (20) ( )

CONSOLIDATION TOTAL (65) ( )

CHAPTER FIVE	**MAXIMUM SCORE** 400/400	=	100%
	MY SCORE /400	=	%

HOW DID YOU DO?

Keep a record of your scores as you work through the book. By the time you reach Chapter 5, you should be scoring 70% or above. If you're not, go back, revise the material, and try again! Practice makes perfect.

	My score	Max score	My %
Chapter 1	_____	150	_____
Chapter 2	_____	150	_____
Chapter 3	_____	350	_____
Chapter 4	_____	400	_____
Chapter 5	_____	400	_____